Children's Songs

I CAN PLAY THAT!

Wise Publications
London/New York/ Paris/ Sydney

D0543183

7.95

Exclusive Distributors:
Music Sales Limited
8/9 Frith Street, London W1V 5TZ, England.
Music Sales Pty Limited
120 Rothschild Avenue, Rosebery, NSW 2018, Australia.

This book © Copyright 1993 by
Wise Publications
Order No. AM89953
ISBN 0-7119-3091-0

Music processed by Interactive Sciences Limited, Gloucester
Cover designed by Hutton Staniford
Music arranged by Stephen Duro
Compiled by Peter Evans

Photographs courtesy of:
Ace

Music Sales' complete catalogue lists thousands of titles and is free from your local music shop,
or direct from Music Sales Limited. Please send a cheque/postal order for £1.50 for postage to:
Music Sales Limited, Newmarket Road, Bury St. Edmunds, Suffolk IP33 3YB.

Amazing Grace

Traditional

Slowly

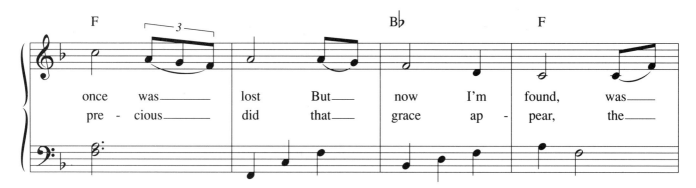

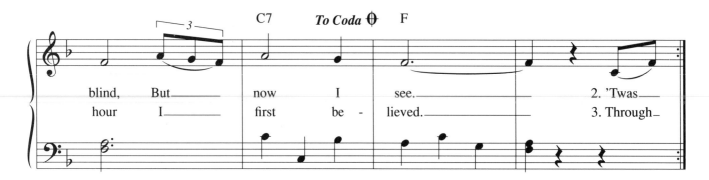

3. man - y_____ dan - gers_____ toils and
4. we've been_____ there ten_____ thous - and

snares, We_____ have al - read - y_____ come_____
years, Bright_____ shi - ning_____ as the_____ sun_____

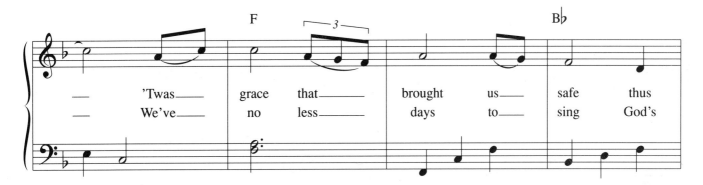

____ 'Twas_____ grace that_____ brought us_____ safe thus
____ We've_____ no less_____ days to_____ sing God's

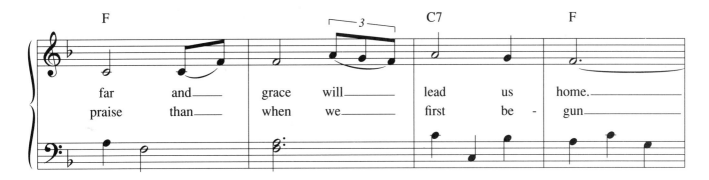

far and_____ grace will_____ lead us home.
praise than_____ when we_____ first us be - gun_____

D.𝄋 al Coda

____ 4. When_____
____ 5. Am -

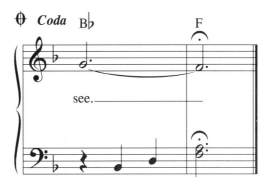

Coda

see._____

English Country Garden

Words and Music by Robert M. Jordan

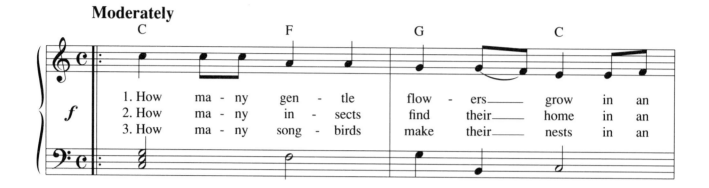

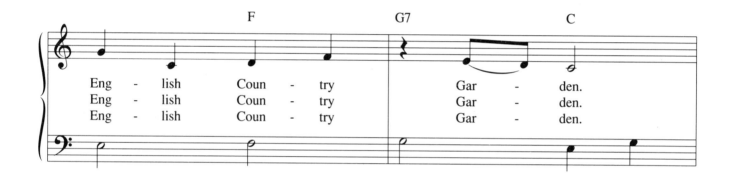

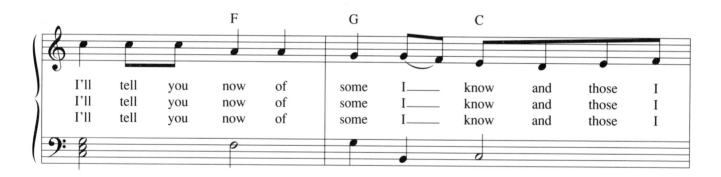

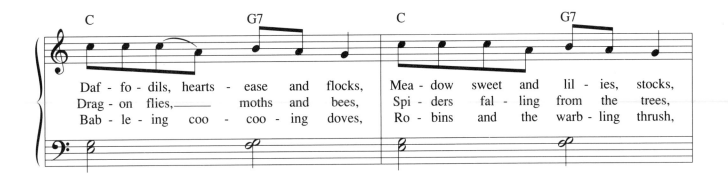

Daf - fo - dils, hearts - ease and flocks, Mea - dow sweet and lil - ies, stocks,
Drag - on flies,_____ moths and bees, Spi - ders fal - ling from the trees,
Bab - le - ing coo - coo - ing doves, Ro - bins and the warb - ling thrush,

gen - tle lu - pin and tall hol - ly - hocks, Ros - es
but - ter - flies sway in the mild gen - tle breeze, There are
blue - bird, lark,_____ finch and night - in - gale, We all

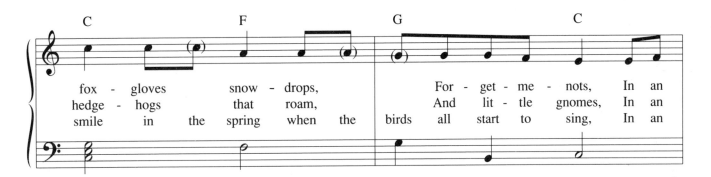

fox - gloves snow - drops, For - get - me - nots, In an
hedge - hogs that roam, And lit - tle gnomes, In an
smile in the spring when the birds all start to sing, In an

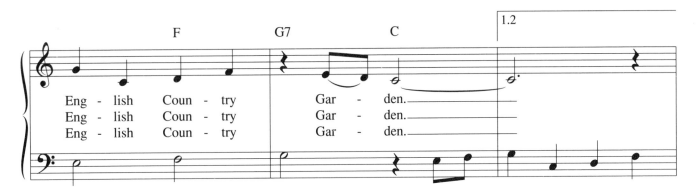

1.2

Eng - lish Coun - try Gar - den._____
Eng - lish Coun - try Gar - den._____
Eng - lish Coun - try Gar - den._____

3.

G7 C

Going To The Zoo

Words and Music by Tom Paxton

Allegro

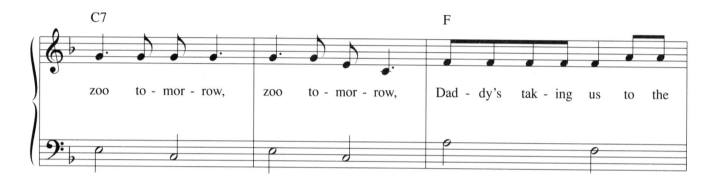

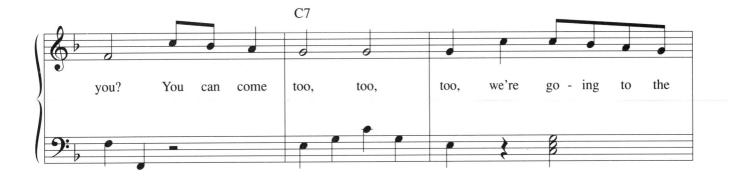

you?   You can come too,   too,   too, we're go - ing to the

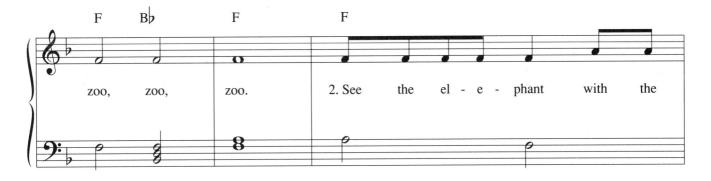

zoo,   zoo,   zoo.   2. See   the el - e - phant   with   the

long trunk swing - in'   Great big ears and   long   trunk   swing - in'

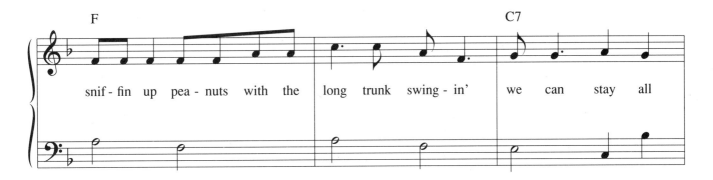

snif - fin up pea - nuts with the   long trunk swing - in'   we can stay all

day. We're go - ing to the   zoo,   zoo,   zoo,   how a - bout

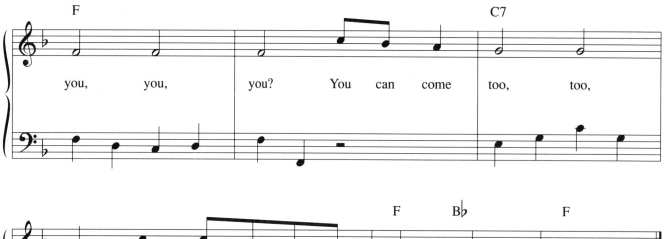

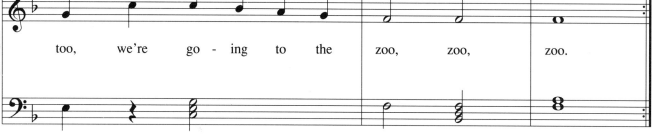

3. See all the monkeys scritch, scritch, scratchin',
   Jumpin' all around and scritch, scritch, scratchin',
   Hangin' by their long tails scritch, scritch, scratchin',
   We can stay all day.
   (*Chorus*)

4. Big black bear all huff, huff, a-puffin',
   Coat's too heavy, he's huff, huff, a-puffin',
   Don't get too near the huff, huff, a-puffin',
   Or you won't stay all day.
   (*Chorus*)

5. Seals in the pool all honk, honk, honkin',
   Catchin' fish and honk, honk, honkin',
   Little seals honk, honk, honkin', (*high pitched voice*)
   We can stay all day.
   (*Chorus*)

6. (*Slower Tempo*)
   We stayed all day and I'm gettin' sleepy,
   Sittin' in the car gettin' sleep, sleep, sleepy,
   Home already and I'm sleep, sleep, sleepy,
   We have stayed all day.
   (*Chorus*)

7. Mamma's taking us to the zoo tomorrow, zoo tomorrow, zoo tomorrow,
   Mamma's taking us to the zoo tomorrow,
   We can stay all day.

   Chorus:
   We've been to the zoo, zoo, zoo,
   So have you, you, you,
   You came too, too, too,
   We've been to the zoo, zoo, zoo.

Ob-La-Di, Ob-La-Da

Words and Music by John Lennon & Paul McCartney

Bright

1. Des - mond has a bar - row in the mar - ket place____
2. Des - mond takes a trol - ley to the jewel - ler's store____
3. Hap - py ev - er aft - er in the mar - ket place____

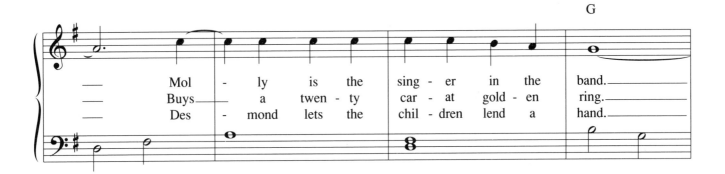

____ Mol - ly is the sing - er in the band.____
____ Buys____ a twen - ty car - at gold - en ring.____
____ Des - mond lets the chil - dren lend a hand.____

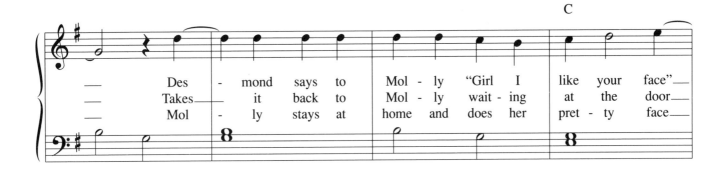

____ Des - mond says to Mol - ly "Girl I like your face"____
____ Takes____ it back to Mol - ly wait - ing at the door____
____ Mol - ly stays at home and does her pret - ty face____

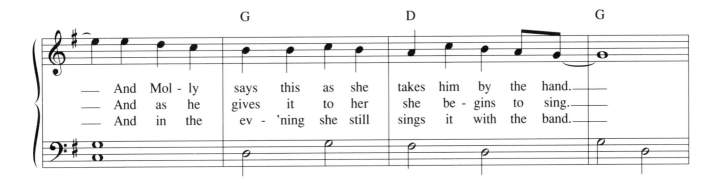

____ And Mol - ly says this as she takes him by the hand.____
____ And as he gives it to her she be - gins to sing.____
____ And in the ev - 'ning she still sings it with the band.____

Ob - la - di___ ob - la da,___ Life goes on,___ Bra___ la___

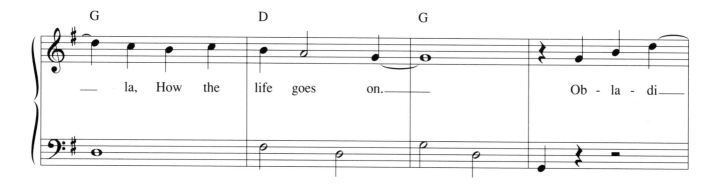

___ la, How the life goes on.___ Ob - la - di___

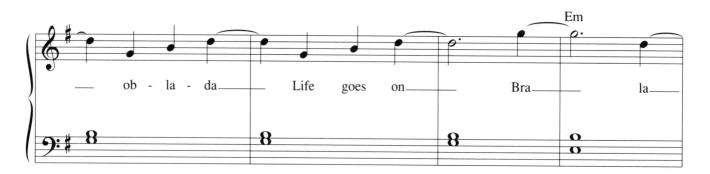

___ ob - la - da___ Life goes on___ Bra___ la

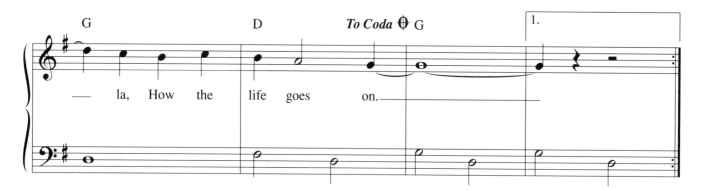

___ la, How the life goes on.___

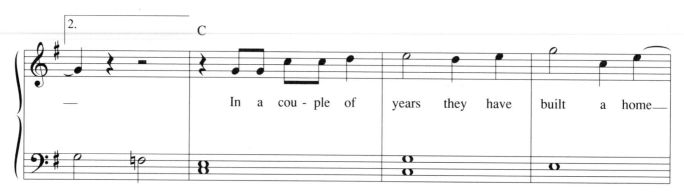

___ In a cou - ple of years they have built a home___

sweet home.

With a cou - ple of kids run - ning in the yard

_ of Des - mond and Mol - ly Jones.

And if you want some fun

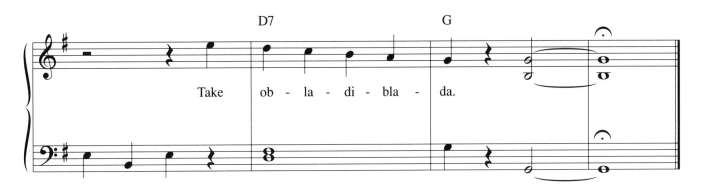

Take ob - la - di - bla - da.

Morning Has Broken

Words by Eleanor Farjeon, Music by Cat Stevens

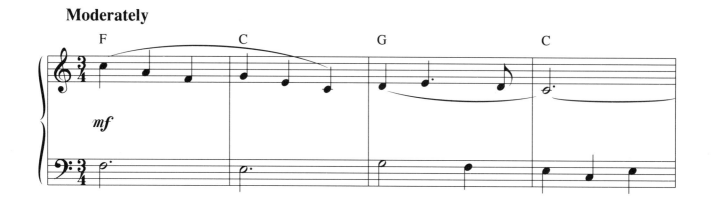

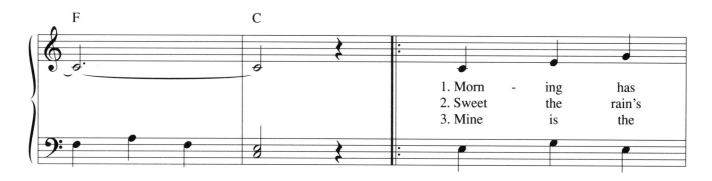

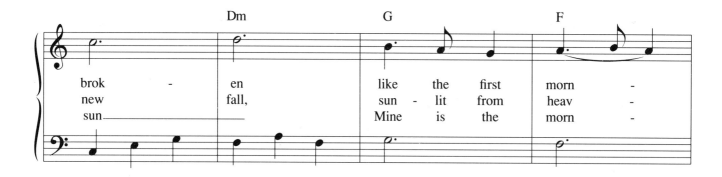

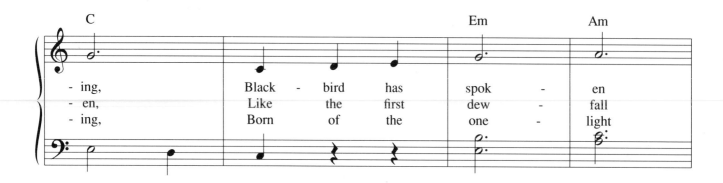

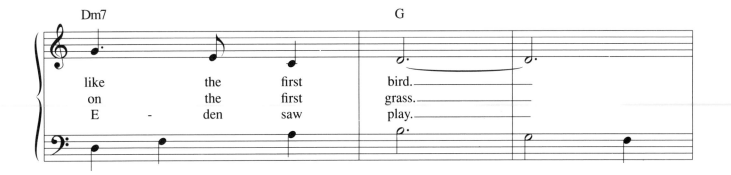

like ____ the ____ first ____ bird.
on ____ the ____ first ____ grass.
E - den ____ saw ____ play.

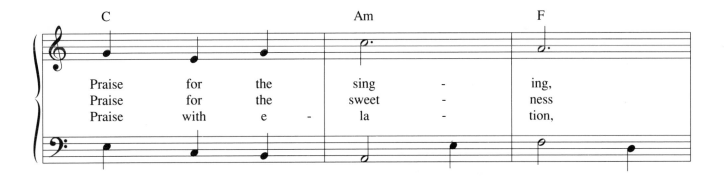

Praise ____ for ____ the ____ sing - ing,
Praise ____ for ____ the ____ sweet - ness
Praise ____ with ____ e - la - tion,

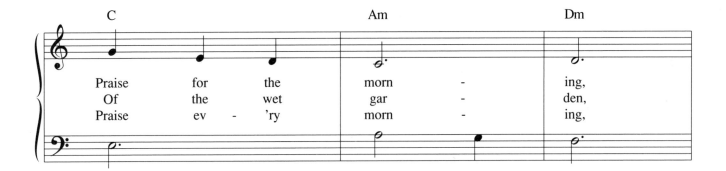

Praise ____ for ____ the ____ morn - ing,
Of ____ the ____ wet ____ gar - den,
Praise ____ ev - 'ry ____ morn - ing,

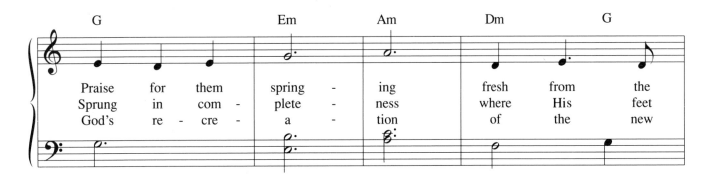

Praise ____ for ____ them ____ spring - ing ____ fresh ____ from ____ the
Sprung ____ in ____ com - plete - ness ____ where ____ His ____ feet
God's ____ re - cre - a - tion ____ of ____ the ____ new

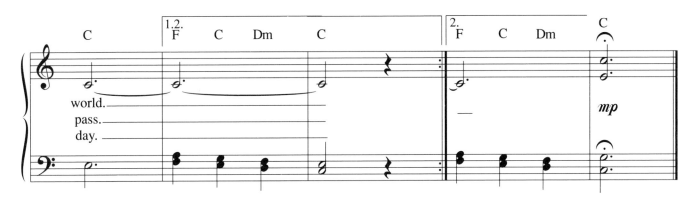

world.
pass.
day.

mp

Puff (The Magic Dragon)

Words and Music by Peter Yarrow & Leonard Lipton

With a lilt

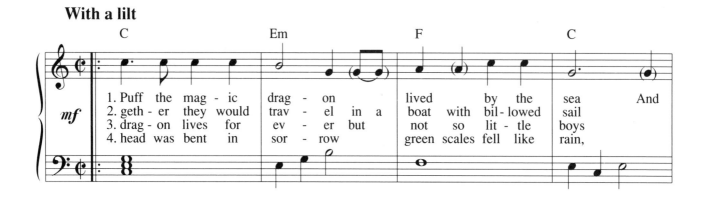

1. Puff the mag - ic drag - on lived by the sea And
2. geth - er they would trav - el in a boat with bil - lowed sail
3. drag - on lives for ev - er but not so lit - tle boys
4. head was bent in sor - row green scales fell like rain,

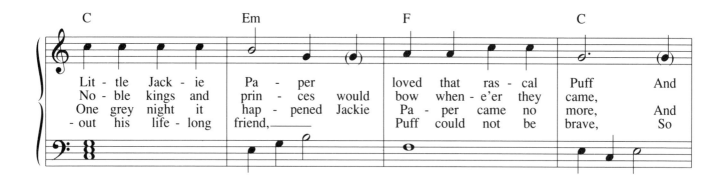

frol - icked in the au - tumn mist in a land called Ho - nah - lee,
Jack - ie kept a look - out perched on Puff's gi - gan - tic tail.
Pain - ted wings and gi - ant rings make way for oth - er toys.
Puff no long - er went to play a - long the cher - ry lane. With -

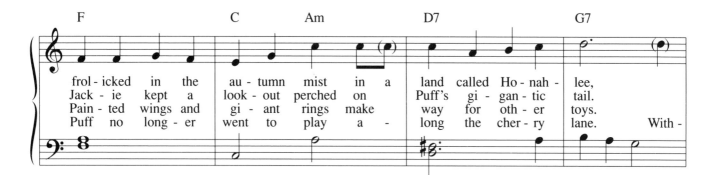

Lit - tle Jack - ie Pa - per loved that ras - cal Puff And
No - ble kings and prin - ces would bow when - e'er they came,
One grey night it hap - pened Jackie Pa - per came no more, And
- out his life - long friend, Puff could not be brave, So

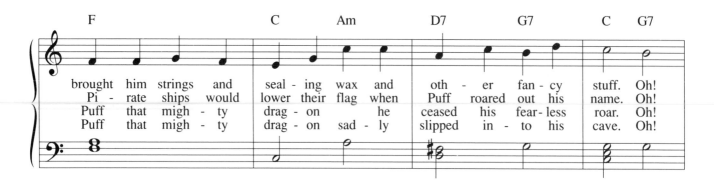

brought him strings and seal - ing wax and oth - er fan - cy stuff. Oh!
Pi - rate ships would lower their flag when Puff roared out his name. Oh!
Puff that migh - ty drag - on he ceased his fear - less roar. Oh!
Puff that migh - ty drag - on sad - ly slipped in - to his cave. Oh!

Chorus

Puff the mag - ic drag - on lived by the sea And

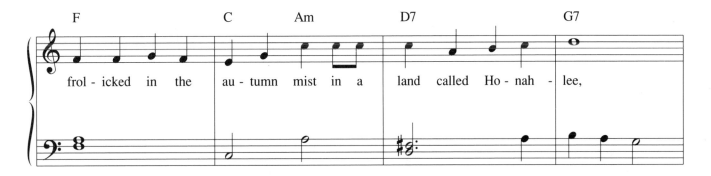

frol - icked in the au - tumn mist in a land called Ho - nah - lee,

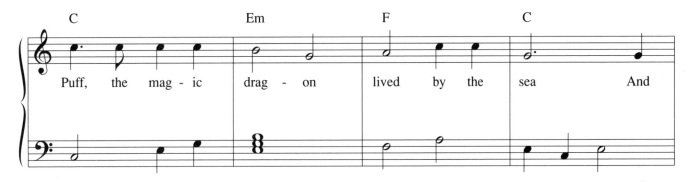

Puff, the mag - ic drag - on lived by the sea And

Last time to Coda

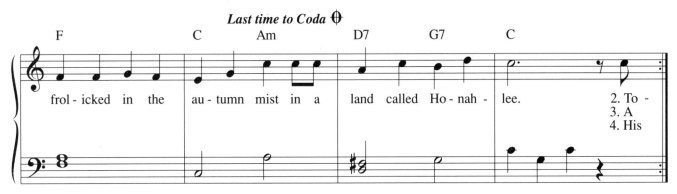

frol - icked in the au - tumn mist in a land called Ho - nah - lee.
2. To -
3. A
4. His

 Coda

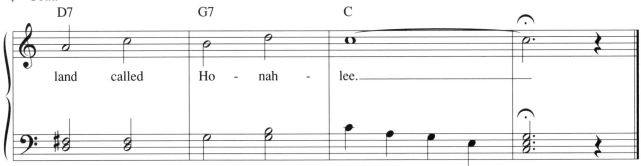

land called Ho - nah - lee.

Little White Duck

Words by Walt Barrows, Music by Bernard Zaritzky

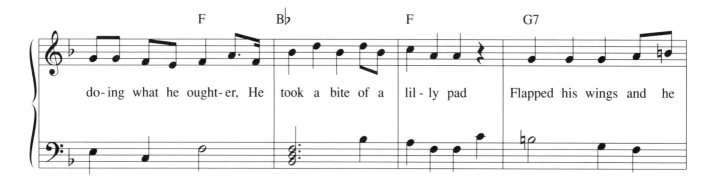

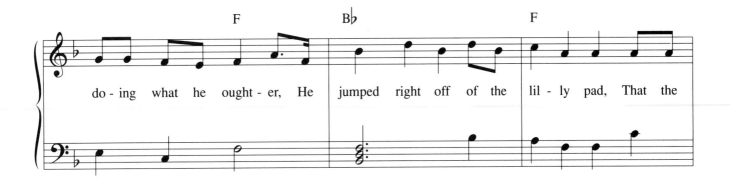

do - ing what he ought - er, He jumped right off of the lil - ly pad, That the

lit - tle duck bit and he said, "I'm glad I'm a lit - tle green frog

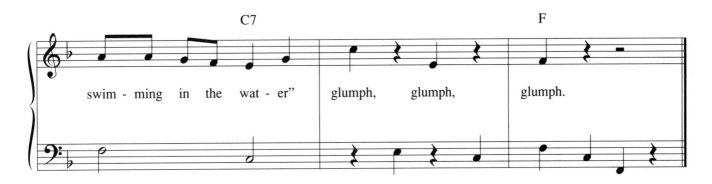

swim - ming in the wat - er" glumph, glumph, glumph.

3. (There's a) Little black bug floating in the water,
   A little black bug doing what he oughter,
   He tickled the frog on the lily pad,
   That the little duck bit and he said,
   "I'm glad I'm a little black bug floating in the water,"
   chirp, chirp, chirp.

4. (There's a) Little red snake lying in the water,
   Little red snake doing what he oughter,
   He frightened the duck and the frog so bad,
   Hit the little bug and he said,
   "I'm glad I'm a little red snake lying in the water,"
   sss, sss, sss.

5. (Now there's) Nobody left sitting in the water,
   Nobody left doing what he oughter,
   There's nothing left but the lily pad,
   The duck and the frog ran away it's sad
   That there's nobody left sitting in the water
   Boo, hoo, hoo.

Three Wheels On My Wagon

Words by Bob Hilliard, Music by Burt Bacharach

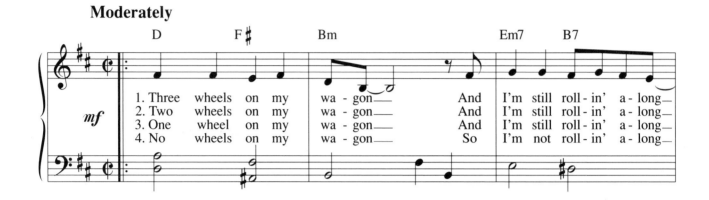

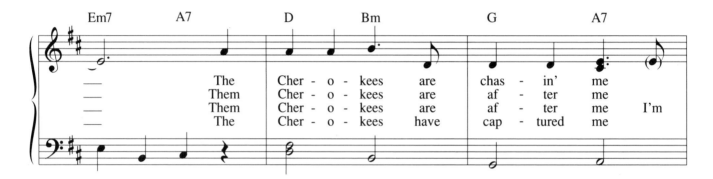

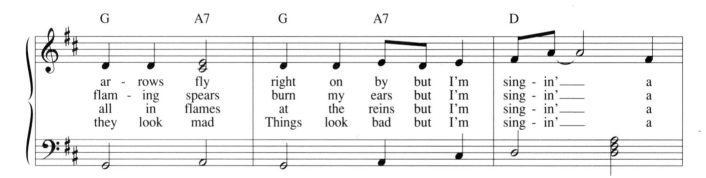

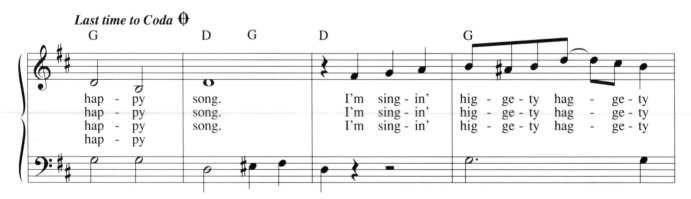

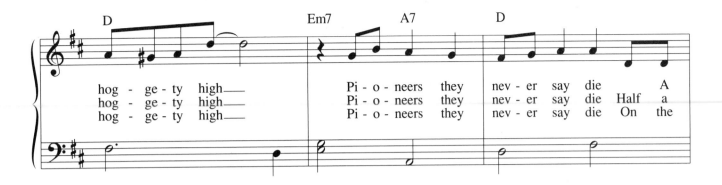

hog - ge - ty high___
hog - ge - ty high___
hog - ge - ty high___

Pi - o - neers they nev - er say die A
Pi - o - neers they nev - er say die Half a
Pi - o - neers they nev - er say die On the

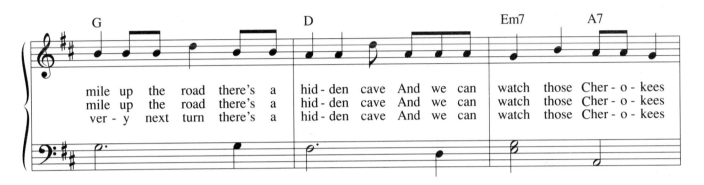

mile up the road there's a hid - den cave And we can watch those Cher - o - kees
mile up the road there's a hid - den cave And we can watch those Cher - o - kees
ver - y next turn there's a hid - den cave And we can watch those Cher - o - kees

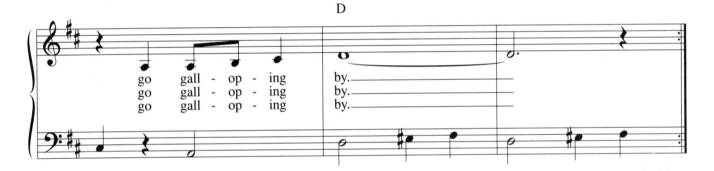

go gall - op - ing by.___
go gall - op - ing by.___
go gall - op - ing by.___

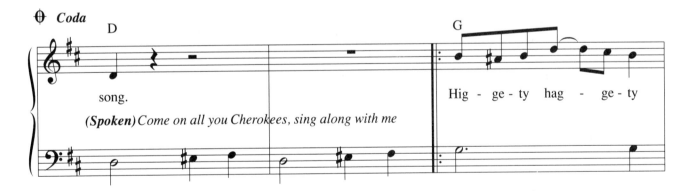

Coda

song.

(**Spoken**) *Come on all you Cherokees, sing along with me*

Hig - ge - ty hag - ge - ty

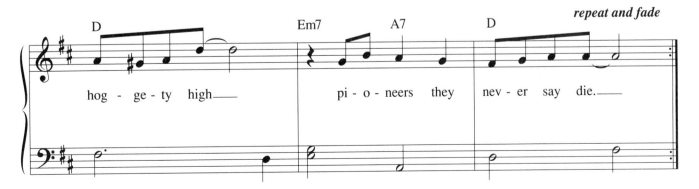

repeat and fade

hog - ge - ty high___   pi - o - neers they nev - er say die.___

When You Come To The End
Of A Lollipop

Words and Music by Al Hoffman & Dick Manning

Moderately

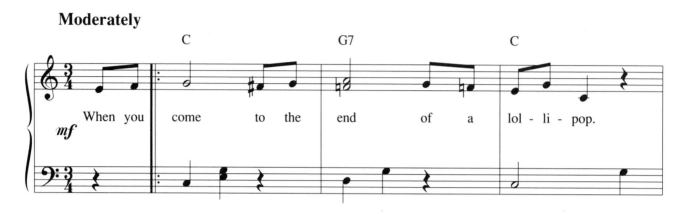

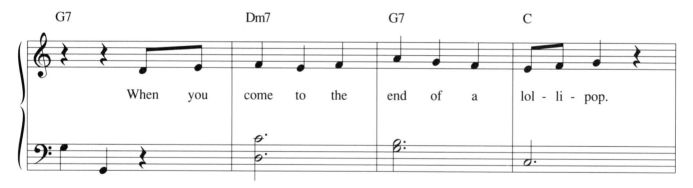

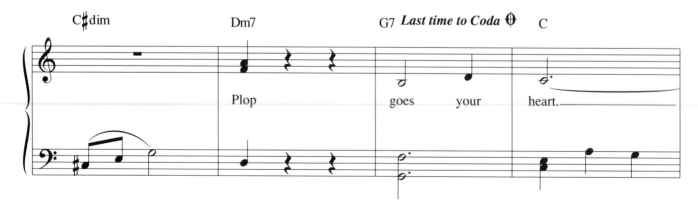

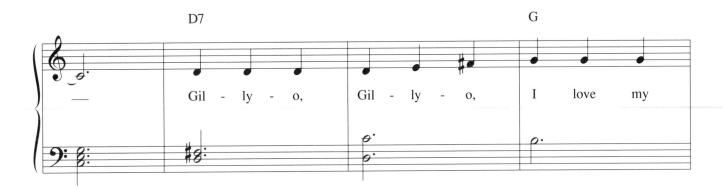

Gil - ly - o, Gil - ly - o, I love my

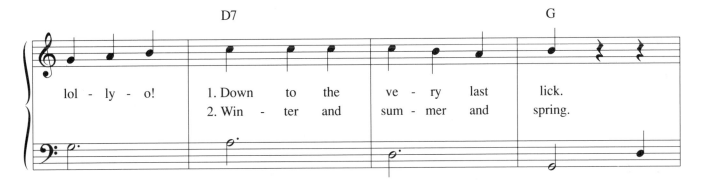

lol - ly - o! 1. Down to the ve - ry last lick.
2. Win - ter and sum - mer and spring.

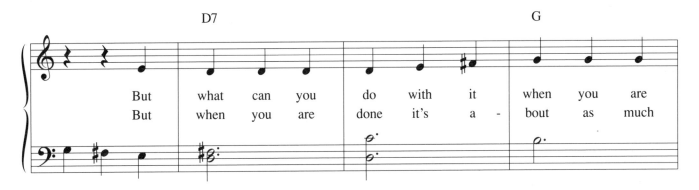

But what can you do with it when you are
But when you are done it's a - bout as much

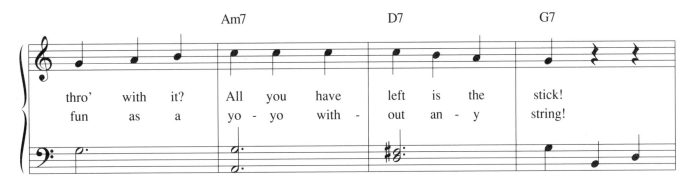

thro' with it? All you have left is the stick!
fun as a yo - yo with - out an - y string!

When you

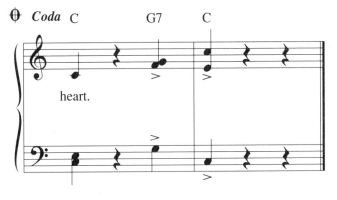

Coda

heart.

23

You're A Pink Toothbrush

Words and Music by Ralph Ruvin, Bob Halfin & Harold Irving

Daintily

You're a pink tooth-brush I'm a blue tooth-brush, Have we

met some-where be - fore? You're a pink tooth-brush, And I

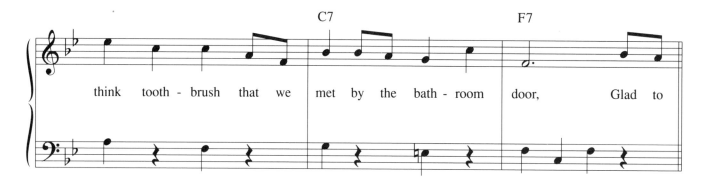

think tooth-brush that we met by the bath-room door, Glad to

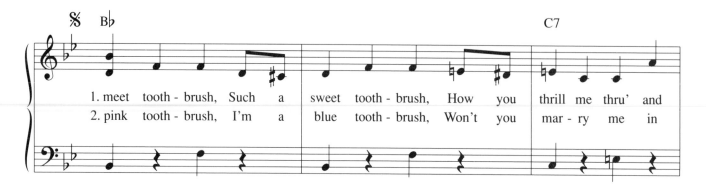

1. meet tooth-brush, Such a sweet tooth-brush, How you thrill me thru' and
2. pink tooth-brush, I'm a blue tooth-brush, Won't you mar - ry me in

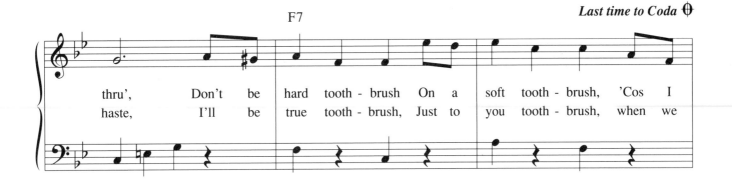

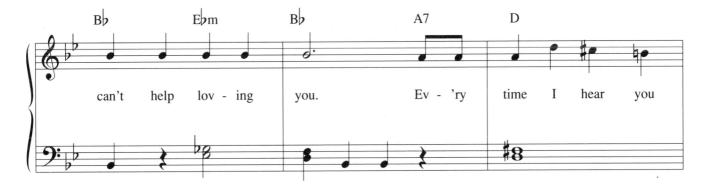

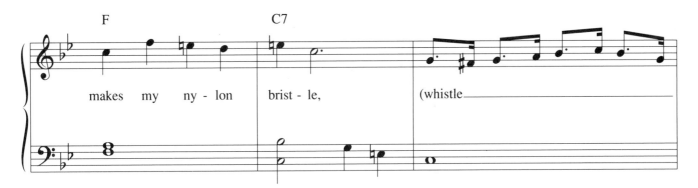

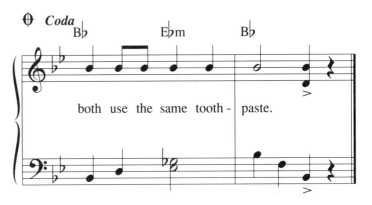

25

I Love Little Pussy

Traditional

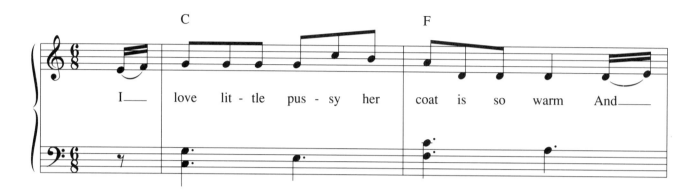

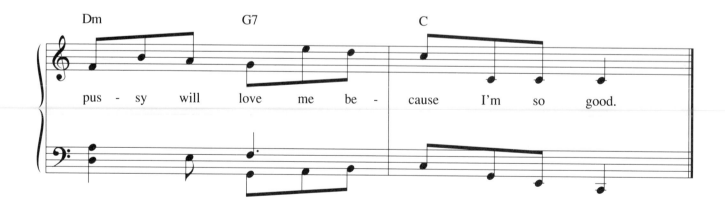

Nellie The Elephant

Words by Ralph Butler, Music by Peter Hart

Moderately

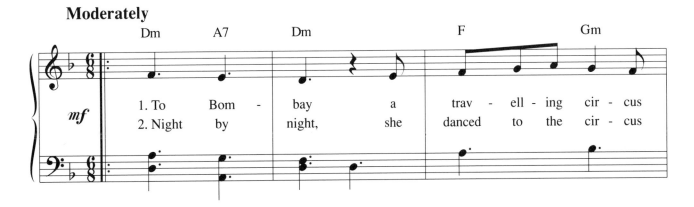

1. To Bom - bay a trav - ell - ing cir - cus
2. Night by night, she danced to the cir - cus

came, they brought an in - tell - i - gent el - e - phant, and
band, when Nel - lie was lead - ing the big pa - rade, she

Nel - lie was her name. One dark
looked so proud and grand. No more

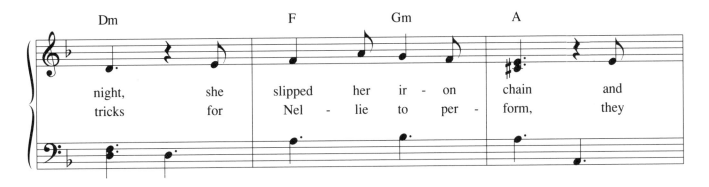

night, she slipped her ir - on chain and
tricks she for Nel - lie to per - form, they

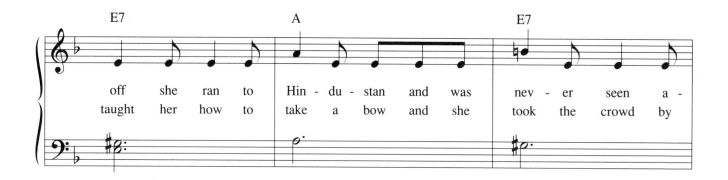

off she ran to Hin - du - stan and was nev - er seen a -
taught her how to take a bow and she took the crowd by

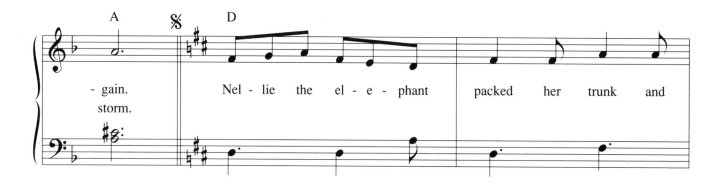

- gain.
storm. Nel - lie the el - e - phant packed her trunk and

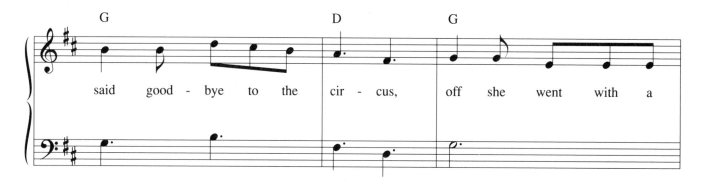

said good - bye to the cir - cus, off she went with a

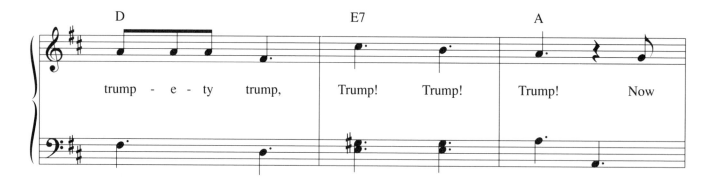

trump - e - ty trump, Trump! Trump! Trump! Now

Nel - lie the el - e - phant packed her trunk and trun - dled back to the

28

To Coda ⊕

jun - gle, off she went with a trum - pe - ty trump,

Trump! Trump! | 1.2. Trump! _____ | 3. Trump! The

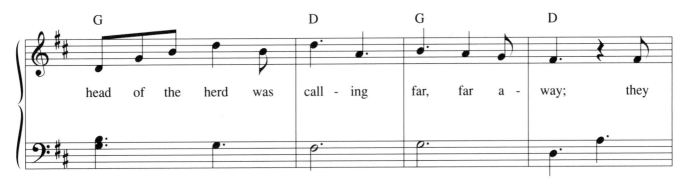

head of the herd was call - ing far, far a - way; they

D.%̸ al Coda

met one night in the sil - ver light on the road to Man - da - lay.

⊕ *Coda*

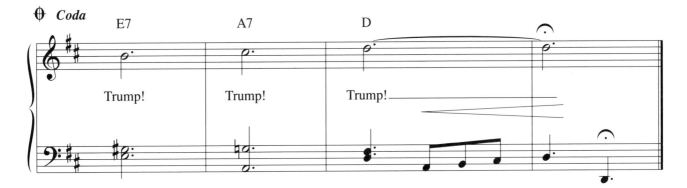

Trump! Trump! Trump! _____

Mary Had A Little Lamb

Traditional

1. Ma - ry had a lit - tle lamb, lit - tle lamb,

lit - tle lamb, Ma - ry had a lit - tle lamb, Its

fleece as white as snow. 2. And ev - 'ry - where that

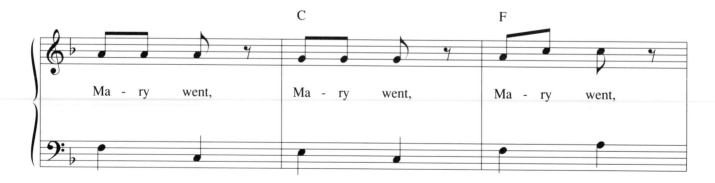

Ma - ry went, Ma - ry went, Ma - ry went,

Ev - 'ry - where that Ma - ry went, The lamb was sure to go.

3. It followed her to school one day,
   School one day, school one day,
   It followed her to school one day,
   Which was against the rule.

4. It made the children laugh and play,
   Laugh and play, laugh and play,
   It made the children laugh and play
   To see a lamb at school.

5. And so the teacher turned it out,
   Turned it out, turned it out,
   And so the teacher turned it out
   But still it lingered near.

6. And waited patiently about,
   'Ly about, 'ly about,
   And waited patiently about
   'Till Mary did appear.

7. Why does the lamb love Mary so?
   Mary so, Mary so,
   Why does the lamb love Mary so?
   The eager children cry.

8. Why Mary loves the lamb, you know,
   Lamb, you know, lamb, you know,
   Why Mary loves the lamb, you know,
   The teacher did reply.

Baa! Baa! Black Sheep

Traditional

Moderately

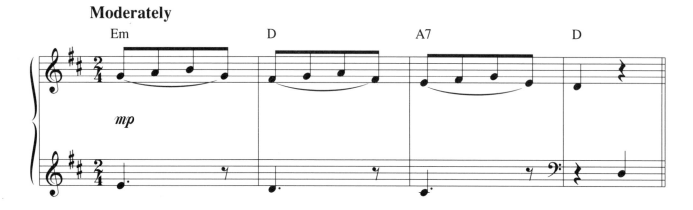

Baa, baa, black sheep, have you a - ny wool?

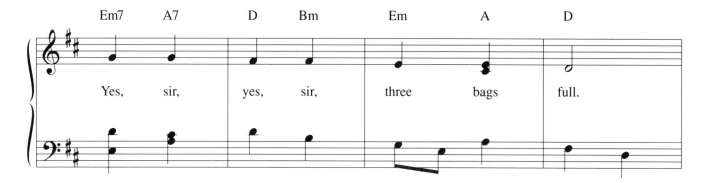

Yes, sir, yes, sir, three bags full.

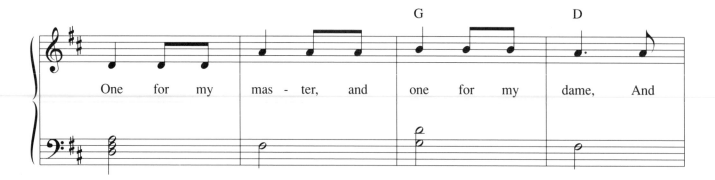

One for my mas - ter, and one for my dame, And

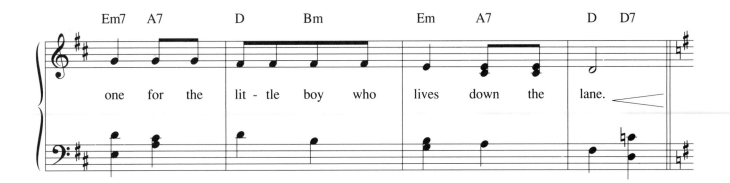

one for the lit - tle boy who lives down the lane.

mf Baa, baa, black sheep, have you a - ny wool?

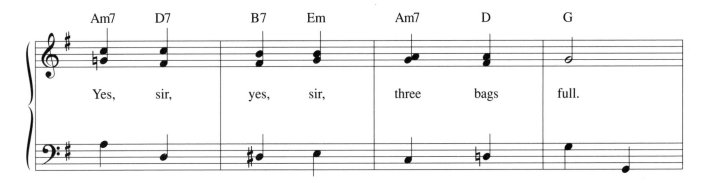

Yes, sir, yes, sir, three bags full.

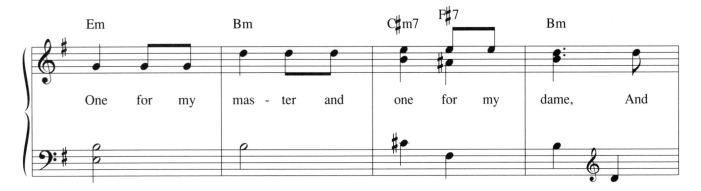

One for my mas - ter and one for my dame, And

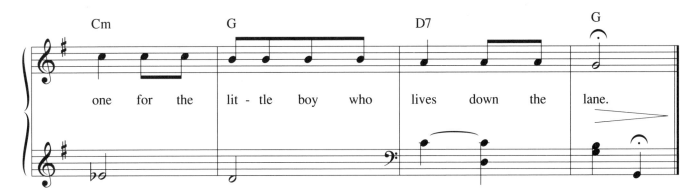

one for the lit - tle boy who lives down the lane.

Froggie Went A-Courtin'

Traditional

Rhythmically

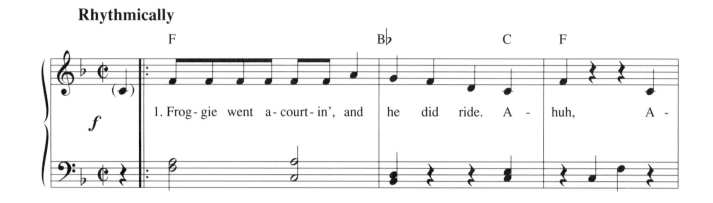

1. Frog-gie went a-court-in', and he did ride. A - huh, A-

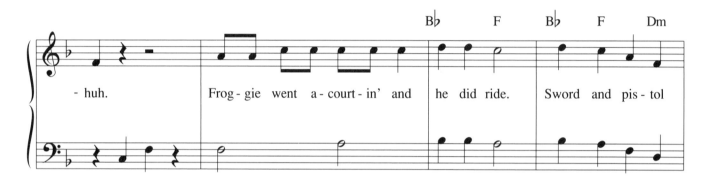

- huh. Frog-gie went a-court-in' and he did ride. Sword and pis-tol

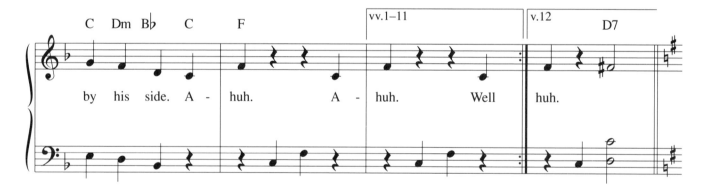

by his side. A - huh. A - huh. Well huh.

That's the end of him and her, A - huh, a - huh.

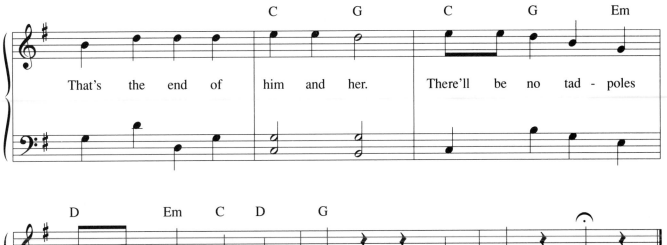

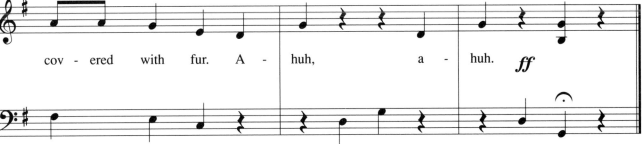

2. Well, he rode down to Miss Mouse's door, a-huh, a-huh,
   Well, he rode down to Miss Mouse's door,
   Where he had often been before, A-huh, a-huh.

3. He took Miss Mousie on his knee, a-huh, a-huh,
   He took Miss Mousie on his knee,
   Said, "Miss Mousie will you marry me?" A-huh, a-huh.

4. "I'll have to ask my Uncle Rat,
   See what he will say to that."

5. Well, Uncle Rat rode off to town
   To buy his niece a wedding gown.

6. "Where will the wedding supper be?"
   "Way down yonder in a hollow tree."

7. "What will the wedding supper be?"
   "A fried mosquito and a roasted flea."

8. First come in were two little ants,
   Fixing around to have a dance.

9. Next come in was a bumblebee,
   Bouncing a fiddle on his knee.

10. And next to come in was a big tomcat,
    He swallowed the frog and the mouse and the rat.

11. Next to come in was a big old snake,
    He chased the party into the lake.

12. That's the end of him and her,
    There'll be no tadpoles covered with fur.

Pop Goes The Weasel

Traditional

Gaily

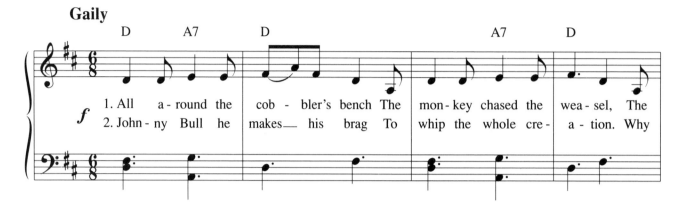

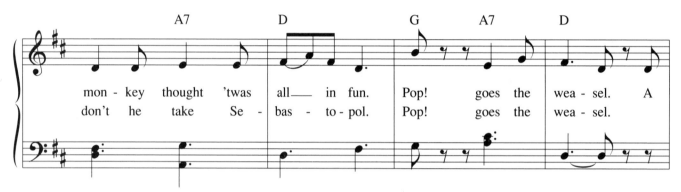

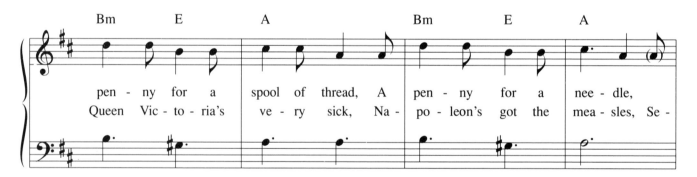

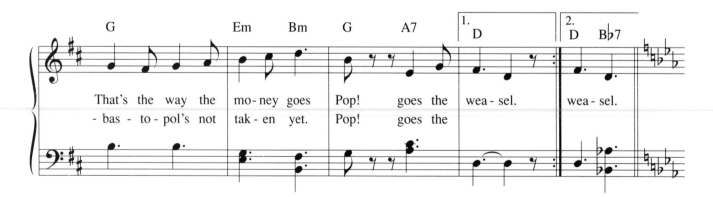

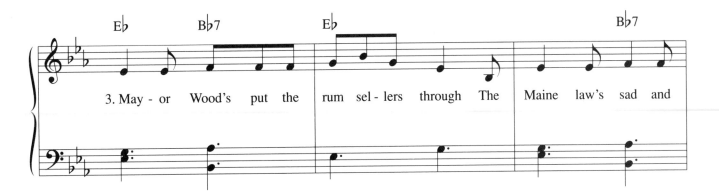

3. May - or Wood's put the rum sel - lers through The Maine law's sad and

ev - il. We can - not get our tod - dy now,

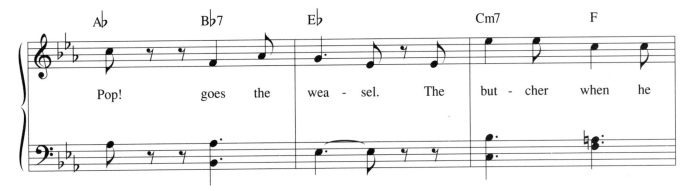

Pop! goes the wea - sel. The but - cher when he

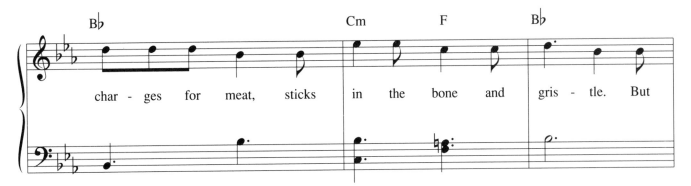

char - ges for meat, sticks in the bone and gris - tle. But

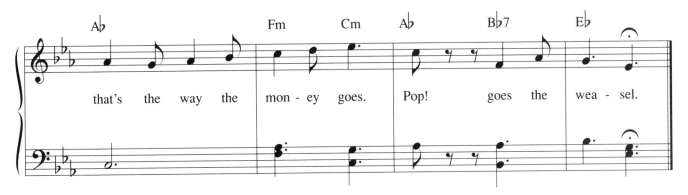

that's the way the mon - ey goes. Pop! goes the wea - sel.

Jimmy Crack Corn

Words and Music by Daniel Decatur Emmett

I was young I used to wait, On mas-ter's ta-ble and serve his plate,

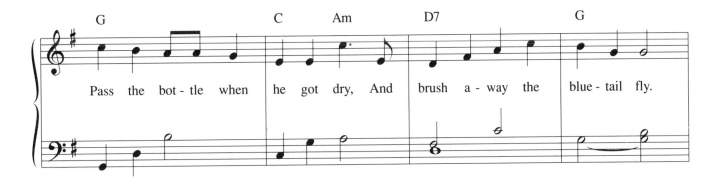

Pass the bot-tle when he got dry, And brush a-way the blue-tail fly.

Chorus

Jim-my crack corn, I don't care, Jim-my crack corn, I don't care,

Jim-my crack corn, I don't care, the mas-ter's gone a - way.

3. Said the blackbird to the crow,
   Down to the fields let us go,
   Eatin' corn has been our trade,
   Ever since Adam and Eve was made.   *Chorus:*

4. Said the Sheldrake to the crane,
   When do you think we'll have some rain?
   The farm's so muddy and the brook so dry,
   If it wasn't for the tadpoles, we'd all die.   *Chorus:*

Old MacDonald Had A Farm

Traditional

Bright

Old Mac-Don-ald had a farm, E - I - E - I -

O. And on that farm he had some chicks,

E - I - E - I - O. With a chick - chick here, and a

chick - chick there, Here a chick, there a chick, ev - 'ry where a chick chick.

Old MacDonald had a farm,
E - I - E - I - O.
And on that farm he had some ducks,
E - I - E - I - O.
With a quack-quack here, and a quack-quack there,
Here a quack, there a quack, everywhere a quack-quack,
Chick-chick here, and a chick-chick there,
Here a chick, there a chick, everywhere a chick-chick.
Old MacDonald had a farm,
E - I - E - I - O.

. . . And on that farm he had some cows . . .
With a moo-moo here, and a moo-moo there,
Here a moo, there a moo, everywhere a moo-moo,
Quack-quack here and a quack-quack there . . .
Chick-chick here and a chick-chick there . . .

. . . And on that farm he had some pigs . . .
With an oink-oink here, and an oink-oink there . . .
A moo-moo here . . .
Quack-quack here . . .
Chick-chick here . . .

. . . And on that farm he had some sheep . . .
With a baa-baa here, and a baa-baa there . . .

Little Bird, Little Bird

Traditional

Lit - tle bird, lit - tle bird, go through my win - dow,

Lit - tle bird, lit - tle bird, go through my win - dow,

Lit - tle bird, lit - tle bird, go through my win - dow, And

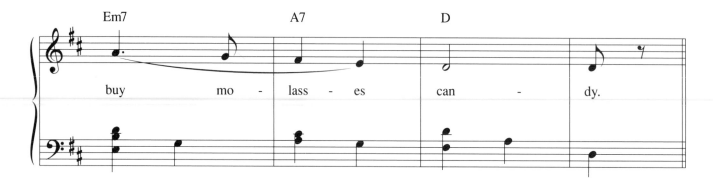

buy mo - lass - es can - dy.

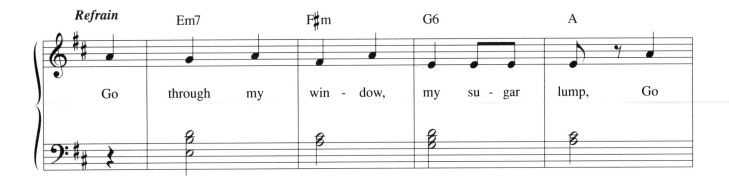

Go through my win - dow, my su - gar lump, Go

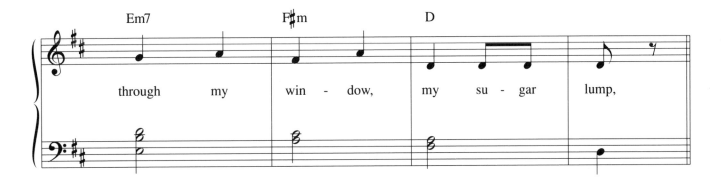

through my win - dow, my su - gar lump,

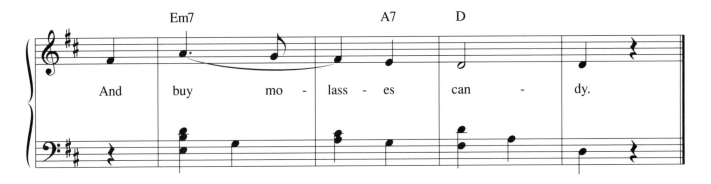

And buy mo - lass - es can - dy.

Blue bird, blue bird,
Fly through my window,
Blue bird, blue bird,
Fly through my window,
Blue bird, blue bird,
Fly through my window,
And buy molasses candy.

Refrain:
Fly through my window,
My little bird,
Fly through my window,
My little bird,
And buy molasses candy.

There Was An Old Frog

Traditional

Allegro

1. There was an old frog and he lived in the spring,

Ching - a chang - a pol - ly mitch - a cow - me - o, He

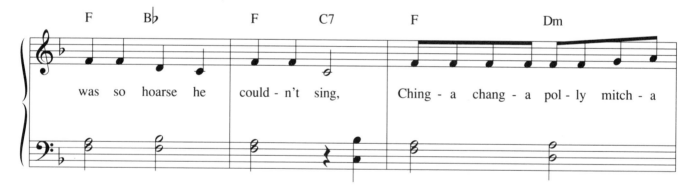

was so hoarse he could - n't sing, Ching - a chang - a pol - ly mitch - a

Refrain

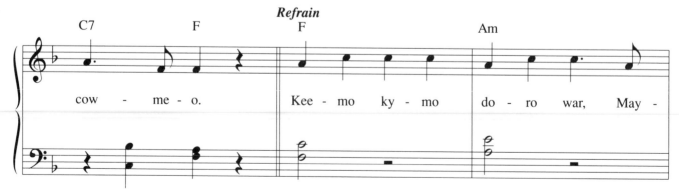

cow - me - o. Kee - mo ky - mo do - ro war, May -

hi, may - lo, my rump - side, pull ma - dell, Pen - ny - win - kle, soap butt, link - horn, nip - cat, Ching - a chang - a pol - ly mitch - a cow - me - o.

2. I grabbed him by the leg and pulled him out,
   Ching-a chang-a polly mitch-a cow-me-o,
   He hopped and he skipped and he bounced all about,
   Ching-a chang-a polly mitch-a cow-me-o.
   Refrain:

3. Cheese in the spring house nine days old,
   Ching-a chang-a polly mitch-a cow-me-o,
   Rats and skippers is a-getting mighty bold,
   Ching-a chang-a polly mitch-a cow-me-o.
   Refrain:

4. Big fat rat and a bucket of souse,
   Ching-a chang-a polly mitch-a cow-me-o,
   Take it back to the big white house,
   Ching-a chang-a polly mitch-a cow-me-o.
   Refrain:

Who Killed Cock Robin?

Traditional

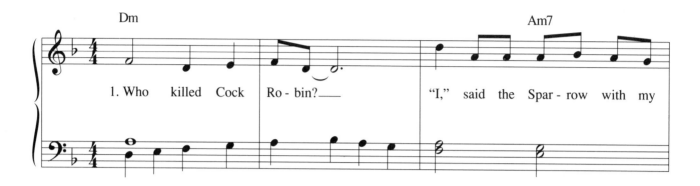

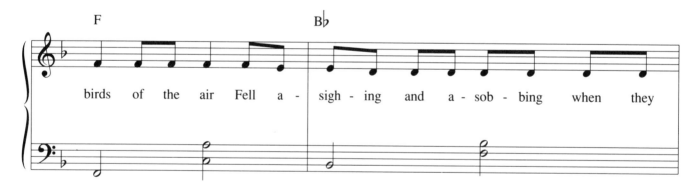

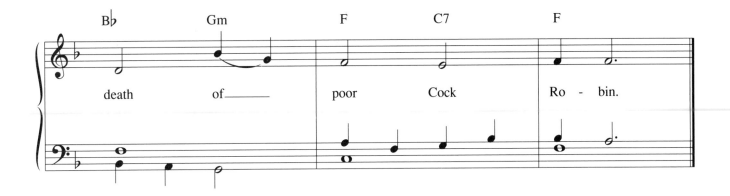

death of _____ poor Cock Ro - bin.

2. Who saw him die?
   "I," said the Fly,
   "With my little twinky eye,
   I saw him die."
   Chorus:

3. Who caught his blood?
   "I," said the Fish,
   "With my little fishy dish,
   I caught his blood."
   Chorus:

4. Who'll dig his grave?
   "I," said the Owl,
   "With my paddock and trowel,
   I'll dig his grave."
   Chorus:

5. Who'll be chief mourner?
   "I," said the Rook,
   "Because I can croak,
   I'll be chief mourner."
   Chorus:

   ***Chorus*:**
   Then the birds of the air
   Fell a-sighing and a-sobbing
   When they heard of the death
   Of poor Cock Robin,
   When they heard of the death
   Of poor Cock Robin.

Three Blind Mice

Traditional

Not too fast

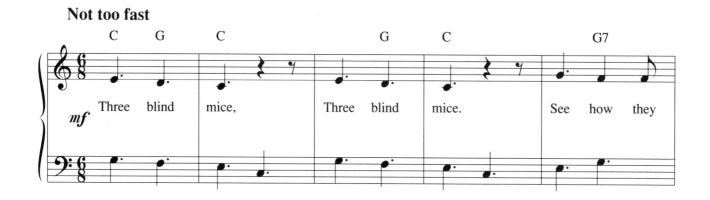

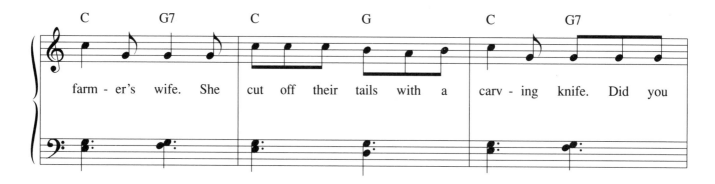

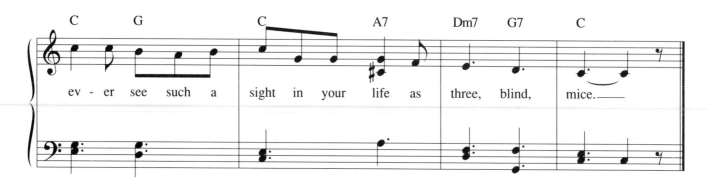